Giant Birds and
Monsters of the Air

Long before there were men in the world, there were giant creatures that flew through the air. Even before there were birds, there were strange animals that could fly. Many, many centuries later man dug up old bones of the strange flying creatures and has been able to get an idea of how they looked as compared to some of the large odd birds of today.

Giant Birds and Monsters of the Air

by William Wise

Illustrated by Joseph Sibal

A
SEE and READ
BEGINNING TO READ
BOOK

G. P. Putnam's Sons  New York

FOUNDED 1838

GPPS

Today, birds are found all over the
world. Some live near the water. Some live
near the mountains.

Some birds live where there are many
trees. Some live where there are almost no
trees.

In every part of the world there are
birds flying about. Some birds even live in
the city and make their nests there.

5

But there was a time, millions and millions of years ago, when there were no birds anywhere in the world.

Instead of birds, strange animals flew in the air. They did not look like any animals you have ever seen.

Some of these strange animals were small.

Some of them were very big.

Some of them were the most terrible monsters that ever flew in the air.

There were no men in the world, millions of years ago. So no man ever saw these strange flying monsters.

But we have found their bones. We have put their bones together. That is how we know what these terrible animals looked like, millions and millions of years ago.

Most of the flying monsters had very long heads.

Some had long, thin tails.

One of them had a long name, too. His name was Rhamphorhynchus *(Ram*-foe-*rin*-cuss).

Rhamphorhynchus lived near the water.
He liked to fly over the water to hunt for
fish.

He had many sharp teeth in his beak.
His sharp teeth helped him to catch the
fish he found in the water.

Ramphorhynchus was safe in the air.
He was not safe on the ground.
He could not run very quickly. He could
not run away from the animals that lived
on the ground.

But Rhamphorhynchus had claws on
both his feet.

He had claws on both his wings.

By using his claws he could climb into a
tree.

There Rhamphorhynchus would sit, safe
from the animals on the ground that
wanted to eat him.

Another flying monster was Dimorphodon (Dy-*more*-foe-don). He had a long tail. He had many sharp teeth in his beak, like Rhamphorhynchus.

Dimorphodon like to catch fish, too.
He liked to open his wings and fly
slowly over the water. Dimorphodon must
have been a terrible-looking monster when
he flew about hunting for his supper.

Some of the flying monsters had short tails. They were called Pterodactyls (*Tare-o-dack*-tills).

The Pterodactyls had long heads and sharp teeth.

They had large wings.

A family of Pterodactyls often lived
together. They flew together over the
water to hunt for fish.

At night they flew into the trees. There
they hung, upside down, by their claws.
They went to sleep upside down, a family
of monsters hanging together in the dark.

The biggest flying animal of all was Pteranodon (Tare-*an*-o-*don*).

His head was almost three feet long.

His wings were very big. They were almost as big as the wings of a small airplane. From end to end they were more than twenty feet long.

Pteranodon was the most terrible monster that flew in the warm air, long, long ago.

For millions of years, Pteranodon, Dimorphodon and the other flying animals were the kings of the air.

But after a while, they did not have the air all to themselves.

Among the trees another pair of wings
could be seen. They were the wings of a
strange little bird, called Archaeopteryx
(*Are*-key-*op*-ta-ricks).

Archaeopteryx was the first bird in the world.

He had small teeth in his beak.

He had a long tail.

He had claws on his feet and claws on his wings.

He did not fly very well. He could climb
a tree much better than he could fly. This
was strange. But after all, Archaeopteryx
was a very strange little bird.

Then, millions of years went by. The world grew colder. The flying monsters began to die off.

One day, Pteranodon, Dimorphodon and all of the others were gone from the world. No animals like them have ever been seen again.

One day, Archaeopteryx died off, too.
But by that time, other birds had come to
take his place.

These new birds were the great-great-
grandchildren of strange little Archaeopteryx. For he was the great-great-grand-
father of every bird that ever flew in the
air or ran along the ground.

In time, some of these new birds grew very big.

They grew very heavy, too. They grew so heavy that they no longer could fly. They were giant birds that always lived on the ground.

Some of these giant birds were terrible monsters. One of the most terrible was Diatryma (*Dy*-a-*try*-ma).

Diatryma was eight feet high.

He never flew off the ground. He was much too heavy to fly.

Diatryma ate any animal he could catch.
He could run quickly over the ground.
So when Diatryma went out to hunt, all
the animals ran away.

Phororhacos (*Foe*-roe-*ray*-coss) was another giant bird. He was bigger and more terrible than Diatryma.

Phororhacos was ten feet high. He was
almost twice as tall as a tall man.

His head was more than two feet long.

He had a large beak.

He had three claws on each of his feet.

Phororhacos ate animals and snakes.

No animal or snake could hope to win a fight with Phororhacos. So, when they saw him coming, the animals tried to run away. And the snakes tried to hide from this terrible giant bird that wanted to eat them.

Diatryma and Phororhacos died off long
before there were any men in the world.
After they died off, millions of years
passed again. By the time the first men
had come into the world, other giant
birds were there, to take the place of
Diatryma and Phororhacos.

These new giants lived on the ground. They were far too big and far too heavy to fly.

Their legs were big and strong. They
needed their legs to carry them over the
ground.

One of these new giants was the Elephant bird. He was ten feet tall.

The Elephant bird's head was very small. But his eggs were very big. Each egg of the Elephant bird was almost two hundred times as big as the egg of a hen.

The Elephant bird was almost twice as
tall as a man. Another bird was even taller.

The Moa (*Moe*-a) was two or three feet taller than the Elephant bird. His legs were bigger, too. The Moa was the biggest of all the giant birds that ever lived.

The Moa and the Elephant bird ate only soft things.

They did not eat snakes.

They did not eat animals.

So, when a Moa or an Elephant bird
saw a man, they did not try to eat him.
This was very lucky for the man. It would
not be nice to meet a giant bird that
wanted to eat you.

The Moa and the Elephant bird lived for a long time. Then they died off. By the time they died off, men had begun to make up stories about them.

As the years went by, men told these stories over and over again. Little by little, the stories changed. They became fairy tales about giant birds that flew in the air. Or they became fairy tales about terrible monsters with wings.

One of these fairy tales talked about a giant bird called the Roc (Rock).

The Roc lived on an island in the sea. His egg was as big as a house.

The Roc was so big that when he flew
in the air, no one could see the sun. At
least, that's what the fairy tale said about
him.

The biggest of all the fairy-tale birds was the Simurgh (*See*-murg). He was the strongest of all the fairy-tale birds, too.

The Simurgh was so strong that he could pick up an elephant with his left foot. Then he could pick up another elephant with his right foot.

After that, he could pick up a third elephant with his beak. And after that, he could fly off with all three elephants.

Men also told fairy tales about the Griffin (*Griff*-in).

The Griffin was said to be a terrible monster. He was part bird and part animal.

He had the wings of a bird. He had the beak and the claws of a bird.

But he had the feet and the body of a lion.

The Griffin liked to eat any animal he
could catch.

He liked to eat lions very much.

He liked to eat men, too. At least, that
is what the fairy tales said about him.

For many years, men really believed there were monsters in the world like the Griffin. Today, no one believes in fairy-tale monsters. And no one believes in giant fairy-tale birds, like the Roc or the Simurgh.

But even today, there really are giant birds in the world. Some of them, like the Cassowary *(Cass*-o-*were*-e), never fly in the air.

The Cassowary is too heavy. He runs along the ground, and he runs very quickly.

Another giant bird is the Ostrich (*Oss-
tritch*). The Ostrich is taller than a man.
He never flies in the air.

But his legs are big and strong. He uses
his legs to run along the ground.

One of the largest flying birds of today is the Condor *(Con-*door). His wings are very big. From end to end they are more than ten feet long.

There are not many Condors left in the world now.

Maybe you will never see one.

Maybe you will.

If you do see a Condor, you will know
you are looking at more than just a big,
strange bird. You will know you are
looking at one of the last of all the giant
birds and monsters of the air.

Key Words

Beak
Bones
Claws
Teeth

Archaeopteryx
Cassowary
Condor
Diatryma
Dimorphodon
Elephant bird
Moa
Ostrich
Phororhacos
Pteranodon
Pterodactyl
Rhamphorhynchus
Roc
Simurgh

William Wise is the author of:

In the Time of the Dinosaurs
Illustrated by Lewis Zacks

The World of Giant Mammals
Illustrated by Lewis Zacks

Monsters of the Ancient Seas
Illustrated by Joseph Sibal

Giant Birds and Monsters of the Air
Illustrated by Joseph Sibal

Joseph Sibal is also the illustrator of:

The Strange World of Dinosaurs
Written by Dr. John Ostrom

The Strange World of Reptiles
Written by James Norman

The Strange World of Insects
Written by George Bush

The Author

WILLIAM WISE is the prizewinning author of more than a dozen books for young readers. His books on exciting creatures of fact and fiction include *In the Time of the Dinosaurs, The World of Giant Mammals,* and *Monsters of the Ancient Seas.* Among his many books for older children are *The Two Reigns of Tutankhamen,* which received a Boys' Clubs of America Junior Book Award Medal, and *Alexander Hamilton,* a Junior Literary Guild Selection.

The Artist

JOSEPH SIBAL is a natural history artist whose paintings have illustrated semitechnical publications issued by museums. His paintings have also been reproduced in popular magazines, such as *Life.* For Putnam's, Mr. Sibal has also illustrated *Monsters of the Ancient Seas, The Strange World of Dinosaurs, The Strange World of Reptiles,* and *The Strange World of Insects.*